For Gerbilius – the noblest Roman of them all. TD

For the Jobes – Naughtius Maximus. DS

SCHOLASTIC CHILDREN'S BOOKS,
EUSTON HOUSE, 24 EVERSHOLT STREET,
LONDON NW1 1DB, UK

A DIVISION OF SCHOLASTIC LTD
LONDON ~ NEW YORK ~ TORONTO ~ SYDNEY ~ AUCKLAND
MEXICO CITY ~ NEW DELHI ~ HONG KONG

PUBLISHED IN THE UK BY SCHOLASTIC LTD, 2011

TEXT COPYRIGHT © TERRY DEARY, 2011
ILLUSTRATIONS COPYRIGHT © DAVE SMITH, 2011

ALL RIGHTS RESERVED

ISBN 978 1407 11178 0

PRINTED AND BOUND BY TIEN WAH PRESS PTE. LTD, SINGAPORE

2 4 6 8 10 9 7 5 3 1

CONTENTS

SOMETIMES THE WORLD HAS A DREADFUL DAY.
SOMETHING HAPPENS THAT IS...

A DISASTER

A WAR

A MURDER

AN ACCIDENT

But tomorrow won't be better. The world has changed forever and sometimes things only get worse – that dreadful day is just the start of some dreadful years. On one dreadful day in October 1347, a fleet of ships arrived at Messina in Italy. Every one on the ship was either dying or dead. Dreadful day? Villains jumped onto the ships to rob them and caught the terrible disease that had killed the sailors – the bubonic plague. They went back home and spread it. Within a few years almost half the people in Europe were dead.

See? One dreadful day leads to dreadful years of horrible history. And the world was never the same again. Every part of the world has had its dreaful days in history. Usually somebody ended up horribly dead – maybe lots of somebodies! And, when you hear about their dreadful day you can smile and say happily...

I'M GLAD IT WASN'T ME! MAYBE MY DAY ISN'T SO BAD AFTER ALL!

What were the most dreadful days in ancient Rome? There are thousands of them. Tens of thousands. You haven't got time to read about them all ... not if you are busy tripping over cats and learning spelling lists. You need just the top ten – a high-speed trip through horrible Roman history. And you've found that top ten here, you lucky reader.

Let's see. Where shall we start?

THE FIRST DAYS OF ROME

756 BC

ANCIENT ROME IS SO ... WELL ... ANCIENT THAT NO ONE IS SURE WHEN OR HOW IT STARTED. NEVER MIND. IF YOU DON'T KNOW SOMETHING JUST MAKE UP A STORY!

OF COURSE! TWO BROTHERS, ROMULUS AND REMUS, ROMULUS DREW A LINE IN THE SOIL WITH A PLOUGH...

RIGHT, BRUV, EVERYTHING ON THIS SIDE OF THE LINE IS MINE - IT'S MY TOWN AND I WANT TO CALL IT ROM!

OH, YEAH? WHAT YOU GONNA DO IF I CROSS YOUR LINE?

BUT WHEN THEY LANDED...

SEEMS LIKE A NICE PLACE. LET'S STAY HERE!

I'M THE LEADER AND I SAY WE SAIL OFF AGAIN TOMORROW

WE'LL SEE ABOUT THAT...

THE WOMEN COULDN'T FIGHT THEIR TROJAN MEN, BUT THEY COULD BE AS SNEAKY AS A GREEK.

RIGHT, WOMEN OF TROY. THE MEN ARE ASLEEP. WE KNOW WHAT WE MUST DO!

KILL THEM?

WHAT? NO! DON'T BE DAFT. WE MAY NEED THEM ONE DAY. NO, FOLLOW ME...

I'M SO EXCITED I'M WETTING MYSELF!

Of course BOTH stories are probably legends and lies. Rotten Romulus or ruthless Roma, take your pick. But the Romans made 756 BC their year 1. The first dreadful day.

THE **BATTLE** OF ALLIA

309 BC

IN 390 BC, ROME COULD HAVE BEEN DESTROYED FOREVER. ONE ROMAN ARMY COULDN'T SAVE IT. AND A SECOND ROMAN ARMY NEEDED THE HELP OF SOME REAL BIRD-BRAINS TO SAVE THE CITY.

ROME HAD BECOME RICH AND POWERFUL. CELTIC TRIBES FROM THE NORTH SET OFF TO INVADE. THE TOP MAN WAS BRENNUS. FIRST THE CELTS CAPTURED THE CITY OF CLUSIUM - A HUNDRED MILES NORTH OF ROME.

ADRIATIC SEA

LIGURIAN SEA

CLUSIUM

ROME

TYRRHENIAN SEA

THE ROMANS SENT THREE LEADERS TO HAVE A CHAT WITH BRENNUS...

I AM FABIUS. I COME IN PEACE

I AM BRENNUS AND YOU'LL LEAVE IN PIECES IF I THINK YOU ARE SPIES

WHICH WE ARE!

BRENNUS WANTED REVENGE. HE SET OFF FOR ROME WITH HIS ARMY OF CUT-THROAT CELTS. THEY MET AT THE BATTLE OF ALLIA. THE ROMANS WERE SMASHED.

WHAT IS IT YOUR ROMANS SAY? VAE VICTIS, ISN'T IT? 'WOE TO THE DEFEATED!'

THE ROMANS FLED TO A TEMPLE ON THE TOP OF THEIR STEEPEST HILL - THE CAPITOLINE HILL.

WHEN THE BARBARIANS ARRIVED IN THE MAIN SQUARE - THE FORUM - THEY MET ONLY A DOZEN WISE OLD MEN OF THE CITY.

PLACE A DOZEN IVORY CHAIRS IN A ROW IN THE FORUM.

WE WILL FACE THE ENEMY

THE OLD MEN WERE SILENT. ONE BARBARIAN TUGGED THE BEARD OF AN OLD MAN TO MAKE HIM TALK. THE OLD MAN SMASHED HIS WALKING STICK OVER THE CELT'S ARM.
OOOOH! THAT HURT, GRANDAD!
WHUMP!
TAKE THAT!
SLICE
THE OLD MEN WERE CHOPPED TO PIECES AND THE CELTS SET OFF FOR THE TEMPLES ON THE CAPITOLINE HILL.
VAE VICTIS! KILL THEM ALL!

THERE WAS ONLY ONE PATH UP THE HILL AND A STEEP CLIFF AT THE BACK OF THE TEMPLE, SO IT WAS EASY TO DEFEND. THE CELTS COULDN'T CAPTURE THE TEMPLE.

THE CELTS BURNED THE CITY ... AND ALL THE HISTORY BOOKS. THEY MURDERED ANY ROMAN WHO HAD FAILED TO REACH THE SAFETY OF THE TEMPLE ON THE HILL.

WE'LL WAIT. WE'LL LET THEM STARVE TO DEATH

NO! DON'T KILL ME IN MY OWN HOME! I'VE JUST WASHED THE FLOOR

TOUGH

THE CELTS LEFT BODIES TO ROT IN THE STREETS WHICH STARTED A PLAGUE. THEY WERE DESPERATE TO CAPTURE THE TEMPLE.

THEN THEY HAD A BIT OF LUCK. A ROMAN ARMY LED BY LORD FURIUS WAS TWENTY MILES AWAY. FURIUS SENT A MESSENGER TO CLIMB THE CLIFF TO THE TEMPLE.

THE CELTS SPOTTED THE MESSENGER...

NIGHT FELL. THERE WERE NO ROMANS GUARDING THAT SIDE OF THE TEMPLE.

LOOK! THERE IS A WAY TO THE TOP!

LET'S ATTACK TONIGHT

CLIMB THE CLIFF, KILL THEM ALL!

THERE MAY NOT HAVE BEEN GUARDS, BUT THERE WAS **SOMETHING** WIDE AWAKE AND WATCHING...

HONK HONK

GEESE!

THE GEESE WOKE THE GUARDS AND THE CELTS WERE THROWN OFF THE CLIFFTOP...

I DIDN'T KNOW HUMANS COULD FLY!

THEY'RE FINE ... TILL THEY HIT THE GROUND

AFTER SEVEN MONTHS, THE TRAPPED ROMANS AGREED TO PAY BRENNUS A THOUSAND POUNDS OF GOLD TO GO AWAY. BRENNUS CHEATED WHEN THE GOLD WAS BEING WEIGHED.

VAE VICTIS, MATEY ... WOE TO THE DEFEATED

A COUPLE OF DAYS LATER, LORD FURIUS ARRIVED WITH HIS ARMY AND BATTLED WITH THE CELTS. THE STREETS OF ROME RAN WITH BLOOD. FURIUS HAD TIME TO MAKE A FAMOUS SPEECH...

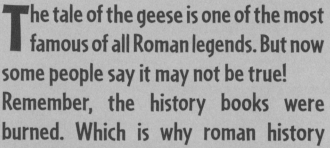

WE DON'T PAY BARBARIANS WITH GOLD - WE PAY THEM WITH IRON ... OUR IRON SWORDS. I'M FURIUS!

I'M NOT VERY PLEASED MYSELF!

THE CELTS WERE MASSACRED. BRENNUS DIED. YOU CAN IMAGINE WHAT FURIUS SAID AS HE STOOD OVER THE CELTIC CORPSE, CAN'T YOU?

VAE VICTIS, CHUM

The tale of the geese is one of the most famous of all Roman legends. But now some people say it may not be true! Remember, the history books were burned. Which is why roman history before 390 BC has a lot of legends. Maybe this is a legend too. The leader of the army in the temple was called Marcus Manlius. He later became one of the most hated men in Rome. He was sent for trial and tried to tell his judges how he had saved Rome ... with the help of the geese. So maybe Marcus Manlius made up that goose story to save his own life?

It didn't work. He was taken back to the top of the temple hill and thrown onto the rocks below.

THE SLAVE WAR OF SPARTACUS

71 BC

THE GOOD THING ABOUT BEING AN ANCIENT ROMAN WAS THAT YOU HAD SLAVES TO DO ALL YOUR HARD WORK. THE MORE COUNTRIES YOU CONQUERED, THE MORE SLAVES YOU HAD. GREAT ... UNTIL THE SLAVES DECIDED TO FIGHT BACK. ALL IT TOOK WAS SOMEONE TO LEAD THEM. SOMEONE LIKE SPARTACUS...

SPARTACUS WAS FROM THE COUNTRY OF THRACE - WHAT WE CALL BULGARIA TODAY.

ROME

BULGARIA

YES I AM A BRAVE BULGAR. BRAWNY

HE JOINED THE ROMAN ARMY BUT THEN DESERTED AND BECAME AN OUTLAW. HE WAS CAPTURED AND SENTENCED TO BE A GLADIATOR - HE HAD TO FIGHT TO THE DEATH IN A ROMAN ARENA.

NOW I AM FORCED TO BECOME A BATTLING BULGAR. BOTHER!

SPARTACUS DID SO WELL THAT HE WAS SENT TO THE GLADIATOR SCHOOL NEAR NAPLES WHERE HE BECAME A GLADIATOR TEACHER - BUT HE WAS STILL A SLAVE.

THAT'S COS I'M A BRUTAL BULGAR. BRILLIANT!

BUT SPARTACUS WANTED TO GO HOME. HE ARMED HIS PUPILS WITH KNIVES FROM THE KITCHENS AND LED A REBELLION.

E TO CHOP
D CHANGE

I LIKE A NICE CHOP

THEY OVERPOWERED THEIR GUARDS, STOLE THEIR WEAPONS AND ESCAPED. THEY MADE CAMP IN THE CRATER OF THE VOLCANO MOUNT VESUVIUS!

I'M A BOILED BULGAR! BAKING!

THE ROMAN ARMY, LED BY CLAUDIUS GLABER WERE HAPPY. THERE WAS ONLY ONE PATH UP THE VOLCANO.

THEY ARE CAUGHT LIKE RATS IN A TRAP. FORWARD, MY LEGION!

BUT CUNNING SPARTACUS SENT HIS SLAVE ARMY TO CLIMB DOWN THE CLIFFS AT THE BACK OF THE VOLCANO. THEY RAN ROUND THE MOUNTAIN AND CAME UP BEHIND THE LEGION.

SURPRISE! SURPRISE!

I GUESS GLABER'S GOOFED

THE SLAVES SMASHED THE ROMANS THEN CAPTURED THE ROMAN CAMP AND PINCHED THE LEGION'S WEAPONS.

I'M A BULGAR BURGLAR. BEASTLY

THE REBEL SLAVES CONTROLLED A HUGE AREA OF LAND. FARMERS AND SHEPHERDS RUSHED TO JOIN THEM.

YOU COULD SAY WE FLOCKED TO JOIN THEIR ARMY

BAA-AA-AAD JOKE

SPARTACUS HAD A REAL ARMY NOW...

NOT A BULGAR'S BUNCH OF BADITS. BEAUTIFUL

GLADIATORS LIKE SPARTACUS HAD BEEN FORCED TO FIGHT AT THE FUNERALS OF RICH ROMANS. NOW SPARTACUS MADE ROMAN PRISONERS FIGHT TO THE DEATH AT THE FUNERAL OF A DEAD ROMAN GENERAL.

IT'S A ROTTEN REBELS' REVENGE

SPARTACUS WANTED TO HEAD FOR HOME.

I LONG FOR MY BROTHER BULGARS. BYE!

SADLY, SOME SLAVES DECIDED THEY DIDN'T WANT TO GO HOME. SPARTACUS'S FRIEND CRIXUS SAID...

LET'S ATTACK THE CITY OF ROME! WE'VE BEATEN THEM ONCE, WE'LL BEAT THEM AGAIN!

CRACKING IDEA, CRIXUS!

SPARTACUS THOUGHT HE WAS MAD TO TRY IT...

SEEMS LIKE A BAD IDEA TO BULGAR. BRAINLESS

CRIXUS LEFT WITH 30,000 OF SPARTACUS'S ARMY. AND, SURE ENOUGH, SPARTACUS WAS RIGHT. CRIXUS WAS KILLED IN A BATTLE WITH THE ROMAN LEGIONS.

YES, WELL, NOBODY'S PERFECT.

WE CAN'T BE RIGHT ALL THE TIME

SPARTACUS BEAT LEGION AFTER LEGION. MANY OF HIS MEN FLED TO THEIR HOMES IN THE NORTH, BUT LOTS OF THEM WANTED TO TURN SOUTH TO ROME.

I AM A BROW-BEATEN BULGAR. IT'S BEASTLY

NOW THE ROMANS SENT A MIGHTY ARMY TO HUNT SPARTACUS DOWN. THEIR LEADER WAS CRASSUS.

I'M THE BOY TO BEAT BULGAR

Spartacus was not a complete failure. Thanks to him, many slaves did escape and get back home to their tribes.
But the cruel Roman executions showed slaves across the Roman world that they couldn't win in the end.

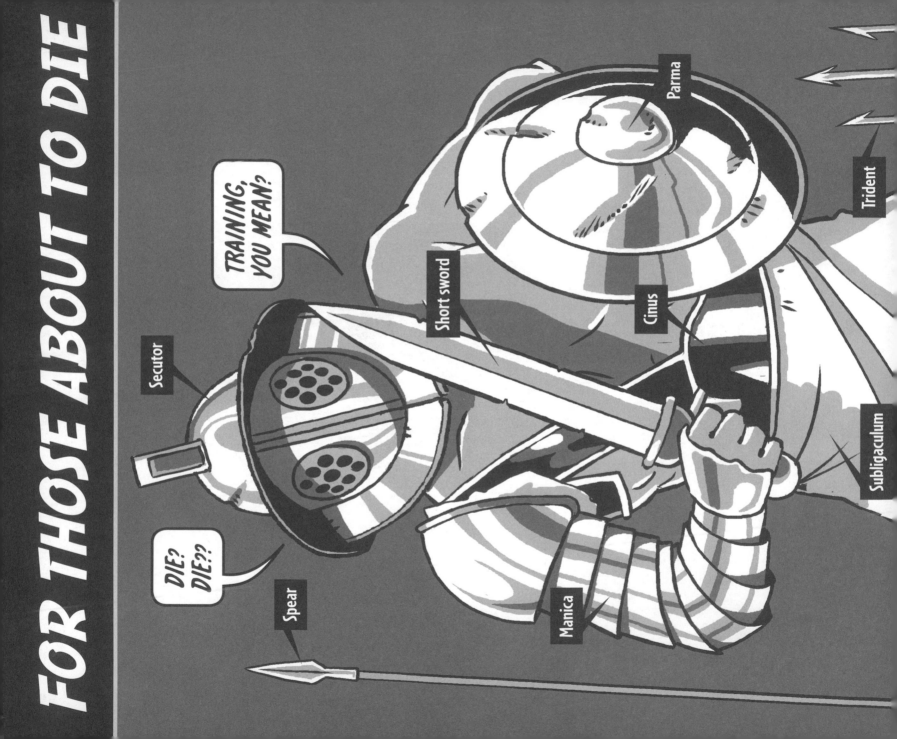

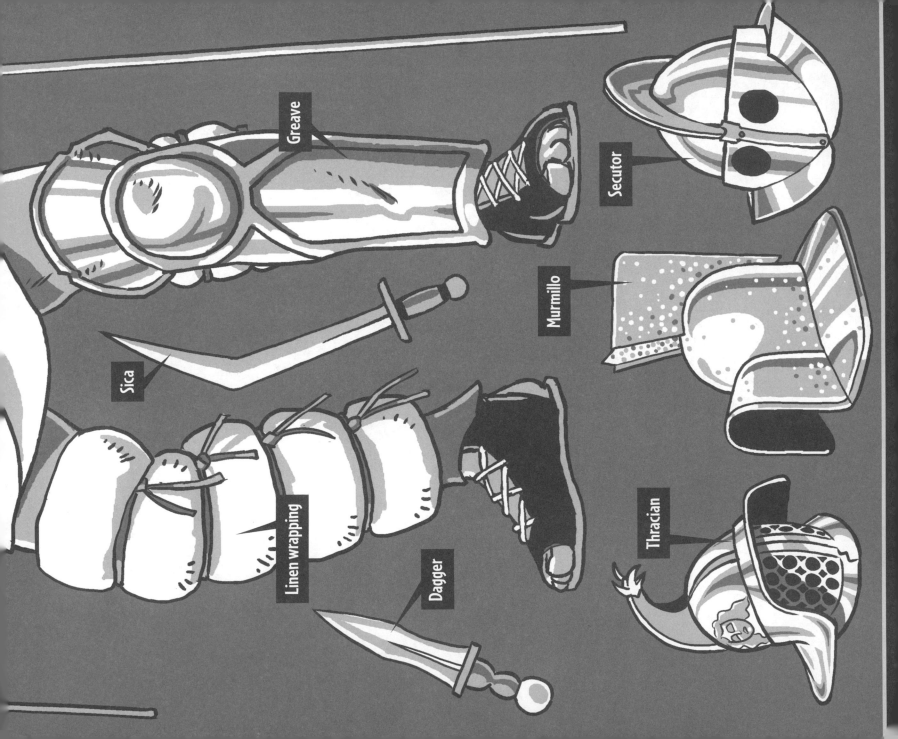

THE BATTLE OF ACTIUM
2 SEPTEMBER 31 BC

THE ROMAN PEOPLE HAD SOME ROTTEN RULERS IN THE EARLY DAYS, SO THEY THREW OUT THE KINGS AND RULED THEMSELVES. BUT AFTER THIS DREADFUL BATTLE THEY GOT SOMETHING WORSE THAN THE KINGS ... THE EVIL EMPERORS.

IT ALL STARTED ON 15 MARCH 44 BC...

JULIUS CAESAR WAS ASSASSINATED! HE WAS STABBED NEARLY 30 TIMES. I READ IT IN MY HORRIBLE HISTORIES BOOK!

THE TOP ASSASSIN WAS CAESAR'S OLD FRIEND, BRUTUS. HE WENT TO WAR WITH CAESAR'S MATE MARK ANTONY AND LOST.

BRUTUS'S HEAD WAS THROWN ON THE FLOOR BESIDE CAESAR'S STATUE. GRUESOME

OUCH!

SERVES YOU RIGHT

DONK!

THE ROMANS SENT FIRE ARROWS INTO THE EGYPTIAN FLEET.

THAT'S FLAMIN' CHEATING!

CLEO PANICKED...

ZZZIMM

SAIL FOR HOME BEFORE THEY SINGE MY LOVELY WIG!

39

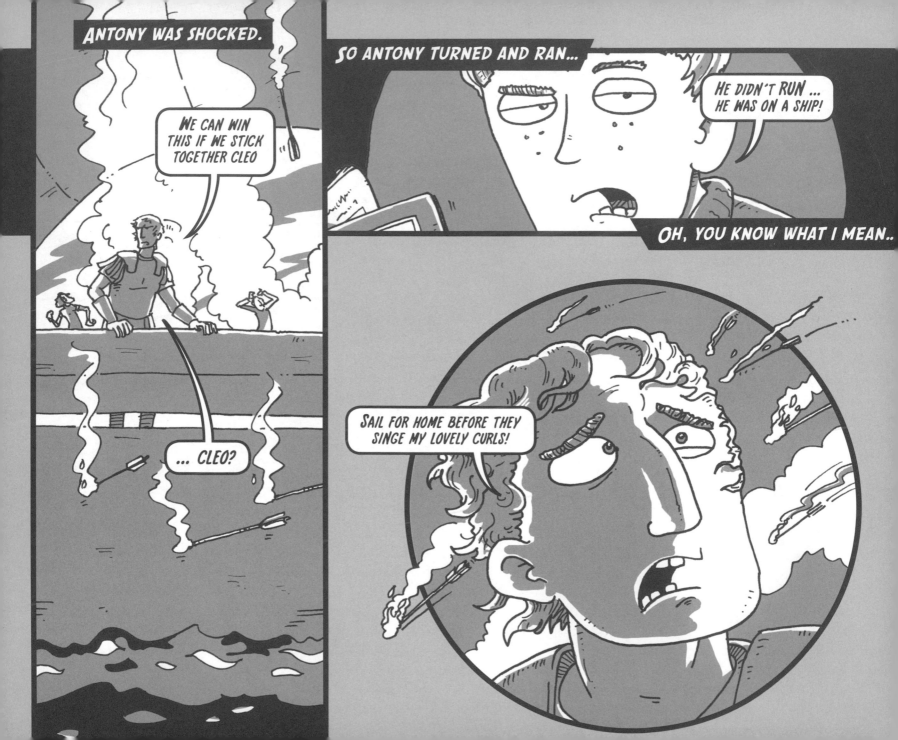

HE HAD HIMSELF CARRIED TO HER.

WHAT A SHAMBLES

GURGLE! I AM DYING CLEO ... DYING ... DY-URRRRGGGGH!

AND HE DIED.

CLEO WAS FINISHED AND SHE KNEW IT.

OCTAVIAN WILL PARADE ME THROUGH THE STREETS OF ROME LIKE A COMMON PRISONER OF WAR. I DON'T WANT THAT. I'D RATHER DIE

SO SHE KILLED HERSELF ... SOME SAY WITH THE BITE OF A SNAKE.

AND NO ONE LIVED HAPPILY EVER AFTER

Cleo was buried with Mark Antony as she had asked. (We don't know what happened to the snake.) Octavian was the top man in Rome now, thanks to that dreadful day at Actium. The Romans had hated their kings but now they made Octavian their emperor. He changed his name to Augustus and became the first of many truly terrible emperors. Evil emperors ruled in Rome. All because of Actium.

POMPEII
24 AUGUST AD 79

The Roman Emperors were mighty men who started to take over the world and turn it into the massive Roman Empire. They took over cities. But sometimes they lived - and died - to regret it. Take the city of Pompeii, for example...

THERE WERE SMALLER EARTHQUAKES. POMPEII WASN'T RUINED BY THEM ... BUT THEY STIRRED UP THE MIGHTY VOLCANO THAT STOOD JUST SIX MILES DOWN THE ROAD ... VESUVIUS. IT BEGAN TO SMOKE A LITTLE...

IT'S THE GOD OF FIRE, VULCAN. HE'S ANGRY! WE'RE DOOMED

YES, I ALWAYS SAID SMOKING IS BAD FOR US

WELCOME BACK, SIR. POMPEII IS NOW AS FINE AS ROME.

WE HAVE FOUR PUBLIC BATHS

ROME HAS MORE

WE GET THOUSANDS OF PEOPLE BATHING IN THEM EVERY WEEK

AH! BUT YOU ONLY CHANGE THE WATER ON A MONDAY MORNING!

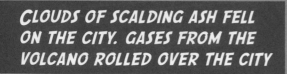

CLOUDS OF SCALDING ASH FELL ON THE CITY. GASES FROM THE VOLCANO ROLLED OVER THE CITY

I CAN'T BREATH!

SOME MANAGED TO FLEE TO SHIPS IN THE HARBOUR. OTHERS TRIED TO HIDE IN THEIR HOUSES

THE HOT AIR IS SMOTHERING THEM. THE ASH IS BRINGING DOWN THE ROOFS!

THERE WERE 20,000 PEOPLE IN POMPEII ... MOST OF THEM DIED.

I HATE TO SAY 'I TOLD YOU SO' BUT I DID. DOOMED! DOOMED! WE'RE ALL DOOMED

THE CITY DIED THAT DREADFUL DAY. THE ASH TURNED COLD AND HARD IN TIME. POMPEII BECAME A CINDER GRAVE FOR SEVENTEEN HUNDRED YEARS. THEN, IN 1748 THE CITY WAS DISCOVERED.

I'VE SEEN THE PICTURES! THEY FOUND THE REMAINS OF PEOPLE IN THE LAST POSITIONS THEY WERE IN WHEN THE ASH AND GAS FELL OVER THEM. THEIR FACES STILL SHOW THE TERROR OF THEIR LAST MOMENTS

Over the years much more of Pompeii has been uncovered. Two million people visit it every year. What a cheerful holiday that must be! Go there and see that carving on the floor ... Salve, lucru – 'welcome to money'.

It should have said 'welcome to death'.

TEUTOBURGER WALD

9 SEPTEMBER AD 9

THE ROMAN EMPIRE CONQUERED AND SPREAD. WHEN IT REACHED THE RIVER RHINE IN NORTHERN EUROPE IT STOPPED. WHY DID IT STOP THERE? BECAUSE ON ONE DREADFUL DAY THE ROMANS MET A CRAFTY ENEMY THAT OUT-THOUGHT AND OUT-FOUGHT THEM.

AUGUSTUS SENT HIS NEPHEW, VARUS, TO DEFEAT THE GERMAN TRIBES. BUT VARUS WAS A FOOLISH MAN.

YOU GERMANS LOVE BEING RULED BY US ROMANS YOU KNOW?

REALLY, LORD VARUS...

OH, YES! ESPECIALLY THAT LEADER OF THE CHERUSCI TRIBE ... WHAT'S HIS NAME?

HERMAN, MASTER.

TWENTY THOUSAND SOLDIERS MADE A LINE THAT STRETCHED OUT OF THE CAMP AND OVER THE HILL. THE SUPPLY WAGONS RATTLED ALONG BEHIND AND VARUS MOUNTED HIS HORSE TO FOLLOW.
ONWARDS. FOR THE GLORY OF ROME!
HERMAN AND HIS CHERUSCI LED THE WAY INTO THE FOREST.
THE TRAILS ARE NARROW. WE ROMANS LIKE TO MARCH SIDE BY SIDE, BUT HERE WE HAVE TO WALK BEHIND ONE ANOTHER
THE ROMAN ARMY MADE A RAGGED LINE, MILES LONG. THE PATHS TWISTED AND FORKED, CLIMBED OVER ROCKY RIDGES AND DROPPED INTO BOGGY SWAMPS.
IF YOU DON'T KNOW THE WAY YOU CAN GO IN CIRCLES FOR DAYS
SCARY THOUGHT

WHEN THE LEADING ROMANS WERE IN THE DEEPEST, DARKEST PART OF THE FOREST THE CHERUSCI RAN OFF INTO THE TREES.

THE CHERUSCI HAVE DESERTED US! THE RATS!

YOU MEAN ... HERMAN THE GERMAN IS VERMIN?

THEN A STORM CAME... THAT WASN'T PART OF THE CHERUSCI PLAN BUT IT HELPED. THE SUPPLY WAGONS BECAME STUCK IN THE MUD AND BLOCKED THE TRAIL. THE ROMANS DIDN'T KNOW THE WAY FORWARD - THE STUCK WAGONS MEANT THEY COULDN'T GO BACK.

STUCK! STUCK! WHAT ROTTEN LUCK

AND THAT'S WHEN THE CHERUSCI, MARSI, CHATTI AND BRUCTERI STRUCK. THEY ATTACKED THROUGH THE TREES AND KILLED THOUSANDS

WHAT ABOUT THE WOMEN AND CHILDREN, HERMAN?

WE WILL SACRAFICE THEM TO OUR GODS

THE ROMANS DO NOT LIKE TO BE MADE PRISONER. THEY WOULD RATHER DIE. SO VARUS FELL ON HIS OWN SWORD. HE KILLED HIMSELF.

STAB! STAB! BLEED! BLEED! OUCHY-OUCH-OUCH!

NEWS OF THE DEFEAT WAS CARRIED BACK TO EMPEROR AUGUSTUS IN ROME. IT DROVE HIM HALF MAD. HE WENT AROUND BEATING HIS HEAD AGAINST THE PALACE WALLS AND CRYING...

OH, VARUS! GIVE ME BACK MY LEGIONS

BONK

SIX YEARS LATER THE ROMANS SENT A NEW ARMY TO GERMANY. WHEN THE ARMY REACHED THE FOREST THEY FOUND HEAPS OF WHITE ROMAN BONES, AND SKULLS NAILED TO TREES. THEIR BOWELS HAD BEEN STRUNG OUT OVER THE TREE BRANCHES.

THE ARMY OF VARUS CERTAINLY HAD SOME GUTS

THEY BURIED THEM.

THAT'S LIFE. TEUTOBURGER TODAY – BEEF BURGER TOMORROW.

A Roman legion had between 4,000 and 6,000 men. Varus had three legions in Germany: the 17th, 18th and 19th legions. Along with their families and servants there would have been around 20,000 men, women and children who went into the Teutoburger forest and died horribly.

NOW HERE'S AN ODD FACT ... THE ROMANS NEVER AGAIN USED THE NUMBERS 17TH, 18TH AND 19TH FOR THEIR LEGIONS – THEY WERE THOUGHT TO BE UNLUCKY.

Herman sent the head of Varus to Marbod, the leader of the greatest German tribe with the message, 'join us in the fight against the Romans. See? We can win!' Marbod sent the head to emperor Augustus in Rome to be buried. Marbod didn't join Herman ... instead he went to war against him. Twelve years later Herman was murdered by his 'friends' from the Chatti tribe.

THE ASSASSINATION OF TIBERIUS

16 MARCH AD 37

ROMAN EMPERORS HAD THOUSANDS OF ENEMIES EXECUTED OR MURDERED. BUT MANY EMPERORS ENDED UP BEING ASSASSINATED THEMSELVES. SOME SAY THE FIRST EMPEROR, AUGUSTUS, WAS POISONED. WE'RE NOT SURE. BUT WE ARE PRETTY SURE THE SECOND EMPEROR, TIBERIUS, WAS MURDERED...

TIBERIUS BECAME EMPEROR IN AD **14**. A ROMAN WRITER CALLED PLINY SAID...

TIBERIUS WAS THE GLOOMIEST OF MEN.

AND A HORRIBLE HISTORIES WRITER SAID HE WAS REALLY CRUEL. AND HE DIDN'T CARE...

I DON'T CARE IF THEY HATE ME ... SO LONG AS THEY OBEY ME.

TIBERIUS EVEN HATED HIS OWN WIFE, AGRIPPINA, AND SENT HER TO PANDATARIA ISLAND WHERE SHE STARVED HERSELF TO DEATH.

BETTER DEAD THAN WED.

BUT YOU DO HAVE TO BE CAREFUL WHAT YOU SAY ABOUT HIM. A POET CALLED TIBERIUS "FAT"

GUARDS! THROW HIM OFF A CLIFF

I SHOULD NOT HAVE CALLED HIM FAT, WHEN THEY THROW ME I'LL GO SPLATT!

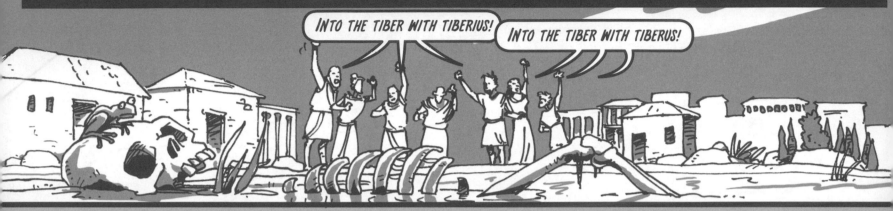

INTO THE TIBER WITH TIBERIUS!

INTO THE TIBER WITH TIBERUS!

IT'S A JOKE, YOU SEE?

BUT NOT A VERY GOOD ONE.

66

A murdered emperor. But a terrible day for Rome, because Caligula turned out to be far worse than Tiberius.

Caligula was mad as well as murderous. But never mind. Caligula himself was assassinated! Stabbed to death by his enemies. Now here's a funny fact...

JULIUS CAESAR **AND** CALIGULA WERE BOTH STABBED ALMOST 30 TIMES BY PLOTTERS. BOTH SETS OF KILLERS WERE LED BY A MAN NAMED CASSIUS. WEIRD, EH?

THE GREAT FIRE OF ROME

18 JULY AD 64

SOME DAYS ARE DREADFUL. BUT SOME DAYS ARE DREADFUL AND THEN GET WORSE. THE DAY OF THE GREAT FIRE WAS BAD, BUT IT WAS JUST THE START OF THOUSANDS OF DAYS OF PAIN AND DEATH. THAT'S HOW DREADFUL 18 JULY AD 64 WAS. THE ROMAN HISTORIAN, TACITUS, TOLD THE STORY...

69

ALL LIES! I WAS IN ANTIUM WHEN THE FIRE STARTED. I DID ALL I COULD TO HELP ... I OPENED MY PALACES TO OFFER SHELTER TO PEOPLE WHO HAD LOST THEIR HOMES. I MADE SURE THERE WAS CHEAP CORN SO NO ONE WOULD STARVE. I EVEN GAVE MONEY TO HELP BUILD NEW HOMES. ROME BURNED - BUT DON'T BLAME ME!

Nero may not have started the fire of Rome but he did make the most of it. He built the huge 'golden house' which had a domed roof that turned at the same speed as the stars. People who lost their homes hated the palace – but so did many rich people, because Nero forced them to pay for it in a very nasty way. He said, 'leave me your money when you die.' when they agreed, he forced them to kill themselves! The fire let Nero build his golden palace – and the golden palace turned all of Rome against him. They drove Nero to his death.

The horrible Roman habit of leaving bodies by the roadside was the death of Nero. He was escaping his enemies at night, with his face covered by his toga. Suddenly his horse scented a corpse by the roadside and reared up in fright. Nero dropped his face cover and was spotted by an enemy. He was stabbed to death.

You could say the fire of 18 July AD 64 was the death of Nero. But the killing of the Christians in the sickening circus went on for more than two hundred years.

THE OPENING of THE COLOSSEUM

AD 80

WHEN THE ROMAN PEOPLE GOT HUNGRY AND BORED, THEY MADE TROUBLE. THE EMPERORS KNEW THEY HAD TO GIVE THE PEOPLE 'BREAD AND CIRCUSES'. BUT THE CIRCUS WASN'T FULL OF CLOWNS AND TRAPEZE ARTISTS. IT WAS A PLACE WHERE YOU WENT TO SEE ANIMALS AND PEOPLE KILLED. BUT ONE DAY WAS BLOODIER THAN MOST...

THE EMPEROR DOMITIAN WAS WEIRD.

MOST ROMAN EMPERORS WERE WEIRD

DOMITIAN LIKED CATCHING FLIES, STABBING THEM WITH THE POINT OF A PEN AND TEARING THEIR WINGS OFF.

SO? WHAT'S WEIRD ABOUT THAT?

TO KEEP THE PEOPLE HAPPY HE FINISHED BUILDING THE COLOSSEUM. A PLACE WHERE ROMANS COULD GO AND WATCH PEOPLE AND ANIMALS BEING MASSACRED.

BUT NO FLIES

ON THE OPENING DAY DOMITIAN BROUGHT IN 5,000 WILD ANIMALS TO BE SLAUGHTERED FOR THE ROMAN PEOPLE TO WATCH.

I AM SO KIND TO ROMANS

BUT CRUEL TO ANIMALS. COULD YOU BEAR TO WATCH?

79

81

THE OPENING OF THE COLOSSEUM WAS THE FIRST OF MANY BLOODY DAYS. EMPEROR TRAJAN CELEBRATED HIS WAR WINS IN AD 107 WITH CONTESTS THAT USED 11,000 ANIMALS AND 10,000 GLADIATORS OVER 123 DAYS.

The Romans made murder into a sport. They built wonderful buildings like the Colosseum, filled them with happy Romans and then massacred thousands of people and animals for fun.

Fifteen hundred years later Christians were visiting the Colosseum to gather the holy sand. The poet Lord Byron (1788–1824) said the Colosseum was 'steeped in the blood of the early Christians who had died for their religion'. (Mind you Byron drank wine from a human skull so he's a right one to talk.)

The Colosseum ruins are still there today. A gruesome reminder of the ruthless Romans and their dreadful days of death.

THE SACK OF ROME
24 AUGUST AD 410

EMPIRES COME AND EMPIRES GO. THE VIOLENT ONES LIKE THE ROMAN EMPIRE GO WITH VIOLENCE. THE TROUBLE WAS THE ROMANS MADE A LOT OF ENEMIES. ONE DAY THEY WERE BOUND TO MAKE AN ENEMY THAT WAS STRONGER AND MORE VICIOUS THAN THEM. ROME HADN'T BEEN 'SACKED' (OR RUINED) SINCE BRENNUS IN 387 BC. IN AD 410 THE ROMANS' ENEMY WAS ALARIC AND HIS VISIGOTHS – AND THIS TIME THERE WERE NO GEESE TO SAVE THEM...

IT STARTED BACK IN **376** BC. A TRIBE FROM ASIA CALLED THE HUNS STARTED TO ATTACK THE TRIBES IN EUROPE, PEOPLE LIKE THE VISIGOTHS. THE VISIGOTHS FLED.

RUN, SON, IT'S THE HUN ... WE'LL GET DONE

RUMBLE

NO FUN

WHERE COULD THEY RUN FOR SAFETY? ACROSS THE RIVER RHINE INTO GAUL, PART OF THE ROMAN EMPIRE.

WELCOME, VISIGOTHS. WE ARE HAPPY TO GIVE YOU SHELTER.

THANKS, MATE.

THE EMPEROR VALENS DECIDED TO ATTACK THE BARBARIAN VISIGOTHS. BUT SUCH CLOUDS OF DUST AROSE THAT IT WAS IMPOSSIBLE TO SEE THE SKY, WHICH ECHOED WITH HORRIBLE CRIES.

SMASH

HORRIBLE CRIES!

HORRIBLE CRIES!

THUD

CRUMP

AND SO THE ARROWS, WHICH WERE RAINING DEATH ON EVERY SIDE, REACHED THEIR MARK. THEY FELL WITH DEADLY EFFECT, BECAUSE NO ONE COULD SEE THEM COMING THROUGH THE SMOKE AND DUST AND NO ONE COULD GUARD AGAINST THEM.

ONE REPORT SAID VALENS WAS KILLED WITH AN ARROW.

ANOTHER STORY SAYS EMPEROR VALENS ESCAPED FOR A LITTLE WHILE...

EMPEROR VALENS ESCAPED TO A NEARBY FARM. THEY TOLD HIM TO SURRENDER, HIS GUARDS ANSWERED WITH A HAIL OF ARROWS

ZONK

TWANG

TWANG
TWANG

THAT'S ONE IN THE EYE FOR THE VALENS

THE ENEMY SET FIRE TO THE HOUSE AND THERE HE WAS BURNED TO DEATH BY VISIGOTHS. HIS BODY WAS NEVER FOUND. THIS DEFEAT WAS THE BEGINNING OF EVILS FOR THE ROMAN EMPIRE.

I SAID IT SPELLED TRUBBELL ... BUT THEY NEVER LISTEN THESE EMPERORS. THEY JUST DON'T LISTEN.

I SHALL SAY A FEW WORDS ABOUT OUR PRESENT MISERY. SAVAGE TRIBES IN COUNTLESS NUMBERS HAVE OVER-RUN US. THE SITY OF MAINZ HAS BEEN CAPTURED AND DESTROYED.

THOUSANDS WERE MASSACRED IN ITS CHURCH. THE ONES WHO ESCAPE THE SWORD DIE IN THE FAMINE.

I'M FAMISHED.

LUCKY YOU!

BUT THE NEXT YEAR HONORIUS DIDN'T PAY UP.

RIGHT, MY VISIGOTHS. LET'S ATTACK ROME AND TAKE WHAT THEY OWE US.

LET'S RACE IN AND SACK THE CITY.

OOOO! GOODY. A SACK RACE.

AND ON **24** AUGUST THE VISIGOTHS STRUCK AND ROBBED THE CITY OF ITS GOLD AND SILVER.

ROB AND PLUNDER.

IT'S A WONDER!

THE TOMB OF THE FIRST EMPEROR, AUGUSTUS, WAS BROKEN OPEN AND ROBBED.

AHEM! AHEM!

WHAT'S THAT?

'IS COFFIN.

93

Soon the Roman empire would be history. Just be glad you didn't live in those days. You could die in a hundred horrible ways. Rome and its empire became not just history ... they became horrible history.

LOOK OUT FOR